Sing
With Elvis!

Wise Publications
London/New York/Paris/Sydney/Copenhagen/Berlin/Madrid/Tokyo

Exclusive distributors:
Music Sales Limited
8/9 Frith Street,
London W1D 3JB, England.
Music Sales Pty Limited
120 Rothschild Avenue,
Rosebery, NSW 2018,
Australia.

Order No. AM975172
ISBN 0-7119-9608-3
This book © Copyright 2002 by Wise Publications.

Music engraved by Paul Ewers Music Design.

CD recorded, mixed and mastered by Jonas Persson.
Guitars by Arthur Dick.
Bass guitar by Paul Townsend.
Drums by Brett Morgan.
Keyboards by Allan Rogers.

Backing vocals by Sorcha Armstrong, Janet Ayres,
Natalie Barowitz and Rob Fardell.

Cover photograph courtesy of Rex Features.

Printed in the United Kingdom by
Printwise (Haverhill) Limited, Haverhill, Suffolk.

www.musicsales.com

Blue Suede Shoes

Words and Music by Carl Lee Perkins

1. Well it's a one for the mo - ney,

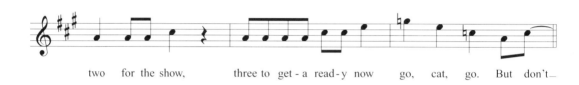

two for the show, three to get - a read - y now go, cat, go. But don't

you step on my blue— suede shoes.—

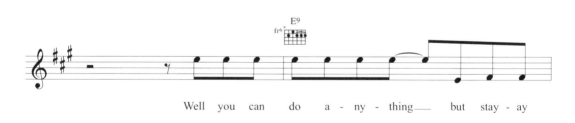

Well you can do a - ny - thing— but stay - ay

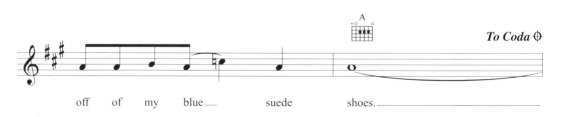

off of my blue— suede shoes.—

2. Well, you can knock me down,____ step on my face,____
burn my house,____ steal my car,____

sland-er my name____ all____ ov-er the place.____ Well, do a-ny - thing____ that you
drink my li - quor from an old fruit jar.____

wan - na do,____ but uh - uh ho -ney lay off____ of { them } shoes. And don't
{ my }

____ you step on my blue____ suede shoes.____

Well, you can do a - ny - thing____ but stay-ay off of my blue____ suede

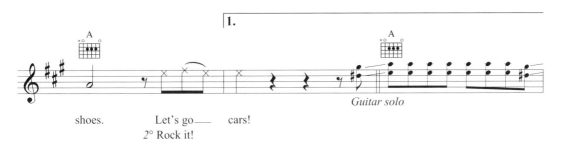

shoes. Let's go____ cars!
2° Rock it!

Guitar solo

5

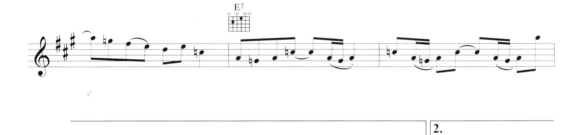

2.

3. Well, you can

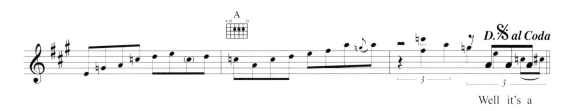

D. 𝄋 al Coda

Well it's a

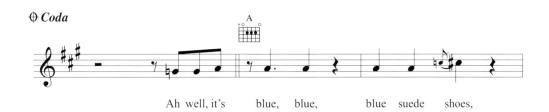

⊕ *Coda*

Ah well, it's   blue,   blue,   blue suede   shoes,

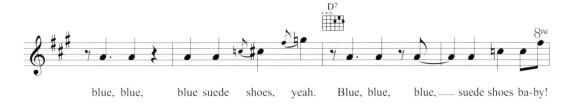

blue, blue,   blue suede   shoes, yeah.   Blue, blue,   blue,— suede shoes ba-by!

Blue, blue,   blue,— suede   shoes.— Well you can   do a-ny-thing— but stay   off—

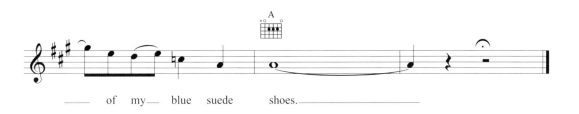

— of my— blue   suede   shoes.

A Little Less Conversation

Words and Music by Billy Strange & Scott Davis

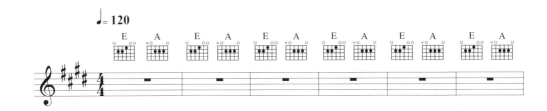

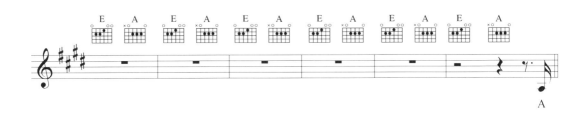

lit - tle less con - ver - sa - tion, a lit - tle more ac - tion please.

All this ag - gra - va - tion ain't_ sa - tis - fac - tion - ing me.   A

lit - tle more bite, a lit - tle less bark,__   a

lit - tle less fight and a lit - tle_____ more spark._____ Close your

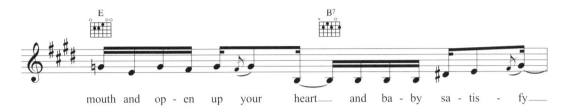

mouth and op - en up your heart_____ and ba - by sa - tis - fy_____

_____ me. Sa - tis - fy_____ me ba - by.

1.

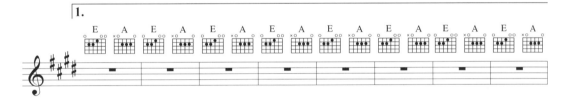

Ba - by close your eyes and lis - ten to the mu - sic dig to the sum - mer breeze._

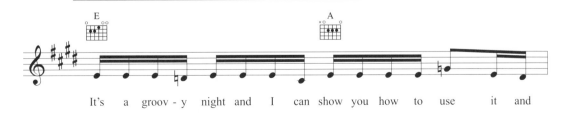

It's a groov - y night and I can show you how to use it and

9

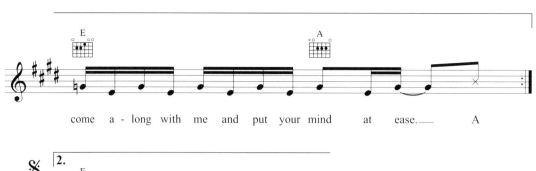

come a - long with me and put your mind at ease.— A

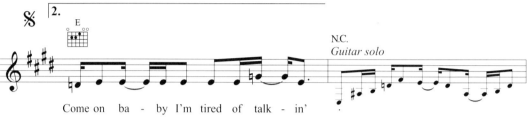

Come on ba - by I'm tired of talk - in'

grab your coat and let's— start a walk - in'.

Come on, come on. Come on, — come on. Come on, — come on.
Come on, come on.

Come on, — come on. Ah, Ah.—
Come on, come on. Don't pro - cras - ti-nate, don't ar - tic - u-late,

Ah.
girl, it's get - ting late, you just sit— and wait a - round. A—

lit-tle less con-ver-sa - tion, a lit-tle more ac-tion please.

All this ag-gra-va - tion ain't sa-tis-fac - tion-ing me. A

lit-tle more bite, a lit-tle less bark,— a lit-tle less fight and a lit-tle— more spark.—Shut your

mouth and op-en up your heart— and ba-by sa-tis-fy— me. Sa-tis-fy

me.

D.%. to fade

One Night

Words and Music by Dave Bartholomew, Pearl King & Anita Steiman

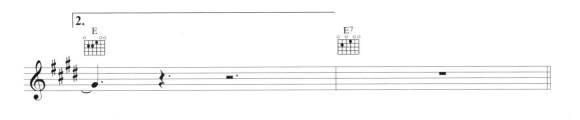

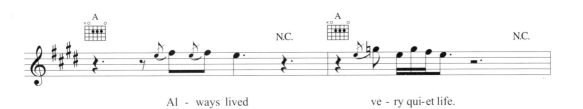

Al - ways lived ve - ry qui-et life.

I ain't nev - er did no_____ wrong._

Now I know___ that life with - out you___ has

been__ too__ lone - ly too long._____ 3. One night___ with

you is___ what I'm___

now   pray - in' for.＿＿＿   The   things＿   that   we＿

＿＿   two＿＿   could plan＿   would＿ make my   dreams＿   come true.＿

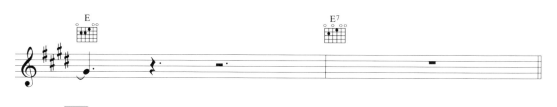

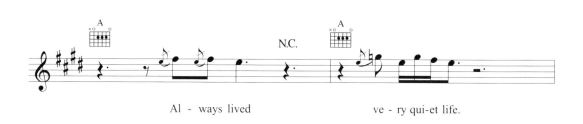

N.C.

Al - ways lived   ve - ry qui-et life.

I ain't nev - er   did no＿＿＿ wrong. ＿

Now   I   know＿   that   life with - out   you＿＿＿   has

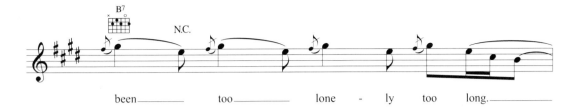

been_____ too_____ lone - ly too long._____

_____ One night_____ with

you   is_____ what I'm_____

now pray - in' for._____   The things__ that we__

_____ two___ could plan___   would_ make my dreams_ come true._

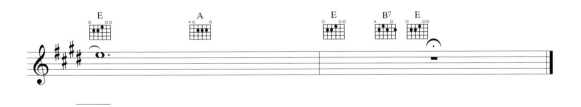

_____

Suspicious Minds

Words and Music by Francis Zambon

1. We're caught in a trap,———
3. So with an old friend I know,———

I can't walk——— out———
a fin - al say hel - lo———

be - cause I love—— you too—— much— ba - by.——————
would I—— still see—— sus - pic - ion—— in—— your—— eyes?—

2. Why can't you see———
4. Here we go a - gain

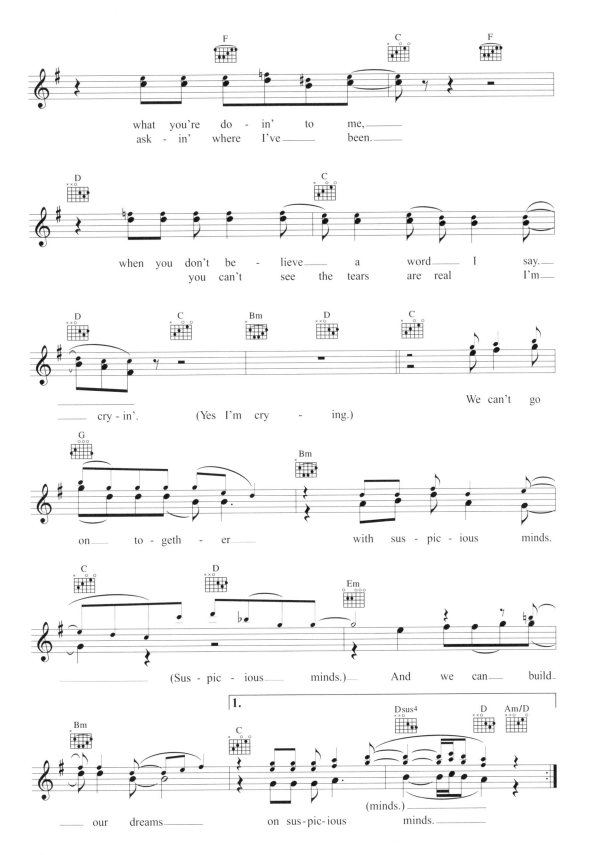

what you're do - in' to me,_____
ask - in' where I've_____ been._____

when you don't be - lieve_____ a word_____ I say._____
you can't see the tears are real I'm_____

_____ cry - in'. (Yes I'm cry - ing.)
We can't go

on_____ to - geth - er_____ with sus - pic - ious minds.

(Sus - pic - ious_____ minds.)_____ And we can_____ build_____

1.

_____ our dreams_____ on sus - pic - ious minds._____

(minds.)_____

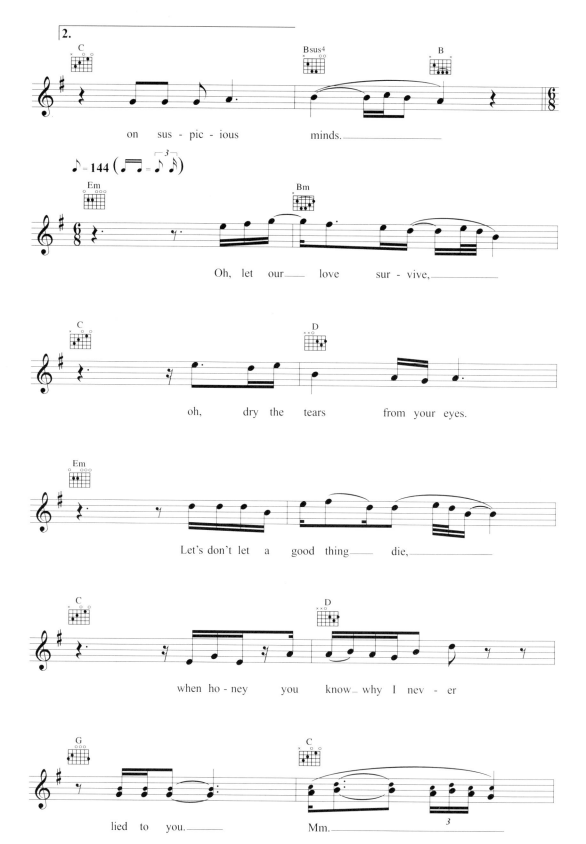

2.

C Bsus4 B

on sus - pic - ious minds.

♩ = 144

Em Bm

Oh, let our— love sur - vive,

C D

oh, dry the tears from your eyes.

Em

Let's don't let a good thing— die,

C D

when ho - ney you know— why I nev - er

G C

lied to you.— Mm.—

It's Now Or Never

Original Words by Giovanni Capurro
Music by E. di Capua
English Words by Aaron Schroeder & Wally Gold

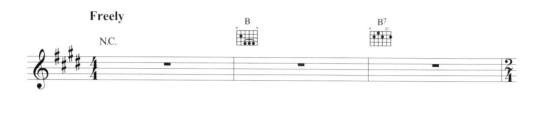

It's now or

nev - er, come hold me tight. Kiss me my

dar - ling, be mine to - night. To -

- mor - row will be too late; it's now or

nev - er, my love won't wait. 1. When I first

saw you, with your smile so ten - der, my heart was
(2.) wil - low, we would cry an oc - ean, if we lost

cap - tured, my soul sur - ren - dered. I've spent a
true love and sweet de - vo - tion. Your lips ex -

life - time wait-ing for the right time. Now that you're
- cite me, let your arms in - vite me. For who knows

near, the time is here at last. ⎫ It's now or
when we'll meet a - gain this way? ⎭

nev - er, come hold me tight. Kiss me my

darling, be mine to - night. To -

- mor - row will be too late; it's now or

nev - er, my love won't wait. 2. Just like a

2.

It's now or nev - er, my love won't wait.

rit. **a tempo**

It's now or nev - er, my love won't wait.

It's now or nev - er, my love won't wait.

more great titles to...

Sing With!

Sing With The Boys!

'No Matter What', 'I Have A Dream'
'Livin' La Vida Loca', 'She's The One'
& 'When You Say Nothing At All'.

24pp. Order No. AM969276

Sing Soul!

'I Got You (I Feel Good)'
'In The Midnight Hour',
'(Sittin' On) The Dock Of The Bay'
'Stand By Me' & 'Take Me To The River'.

24pp. Order No. AM972180

Sing With Pop Idols!

'Flying Without Wings'
'Evergreen', 'Unchained Melody'
'Mack The Knife' & 'Yesterday'.

24pp. Order No. AM974116

Sing With Robbie!

'Angels', 'Strong'
'Supreme', 'Rock DJ'
& 'She's The One'.

24pp. Order No. AM969947

CD Track Listing

1 Blue Suede Shoes (Perkins)
Carlin Music Corporation.

2 A Little Less Conversation (Strange/Davis)
Carlin Music Corporation.

3 One Night (Bartholomew/King/Steiman)
Sony/ATV Music Publishing (UK) Limited.

4 Suspicious Minds (Zambon)
Sony/ATV Music Publishing (UK) Limited.

5 It's Now Or Never (Capurro/Capua/Schroeder/Gold)
Carlin Music Corporation.

To remove your CD from the plastic sleeve, lift the small lip on the right to break the perforated flap. Replace the disc after use for convenient storage.